Bert's HALL
GREAT INVEN

CTW
SESAME STREET®

by Revena Dwight

illustrated by Roger Bradfield

featuring Bert and Ernie
and other Jim Henson Muppets

Bert's Hall of Great Inventions was written to help children
become more aware of natural animal characteristics
and see counterparts in man-made machines and tools.
  This educational product was created in cooperation
with the Children's Television Workshop, producers of
Sesame Street. Children do not have to watch the television show to benefit from this book. Workshop revenues
from this product will be used to help support CTW educational projects.

Bert is performed by FRANK OZ
and Ernie by JIM HENSON on SESAME STREET.

A SESAME STREET BOOK

Published by Western Publishing Company, Inc.
in conjunction with Children's Television Workshop.

Tenth Printing, 1981

While Ernie was strolling, one day, in the zoo,
He ran into some friends who were strolling
 there, too.
They walked till they came to a sign that
 was new:

"Just step through this door," shouted Bert,
   "and you'll see
The greatest inventions of all history!
The show is fantastic, and, what's more, it's free!

   "Oh, hi there, Ernie."

*"Hi there,
Bert."*

"Ladies and gents, please watch closely as I
Launch this truly remarkable PLANE toward
the sky.
An amazing invention! A machine that can fly!

*"I'll bet you never saw anything like this
before, Ernie."*

"My bird-friend flew long before your airplane did, Bert."

"Well, then, look over here at *this* nifty device.
It's clever! It's handy! It's useful! It's nice!
It can grab on to things . . . like this cage full
   of mice.

   "It's a PINCERS, Ernie!"

"*My lobster-friend holds on tighter than that, Bert.*"

"Now, Ernie, here's something that's sparkling
    bright.
It helps you to see, when it gets dark at night.
The simply incredible ELECTRIC LIGHT!

   "Isn't that a great invention?"

"Hey, look here, old buddy. This has just
    got to stop!
Now, *here's* an invention that you'll never top.
It can put out a fire; it can water a crop.

   "Presenting the absolutely amazing HOSE!"

"Not bad, Bert—but my elephant-friend has a built-in *hose*."

"When a fly or mosquito is being a pest,
This little gadget will pass every test.
The simplest inventions are often the best . . .

"A FLYSWATTER, Ernie."

"Or a cow's tail, Bert?
That's a good swatter, too."

"Ernie, you're driving me straight up the wall!
Ah, but here's the invention that's best of
  them all.
It's so strong it can move everything in this hall.

*"I'd like to see one of your animal friends
try to match this BULLDOZER!"*

"Bert—Bert! Look out! My goat-friend can do the very same thing!"

"I don't know how to say this, old buddy,
    old friend,
But this animal nonsense has *just reached
    its end!*
'Cause I've got something here on which I
    can depend.

   "No animal ever wore a SUIT OF ARMOR!"

"How about my turtle-friend, Bert?"
He wears his armor wherever he goes.
Not to mention this lovely little
armadillo, here."

"There's no doubt about it. I'll just have to say
That your animal buddies have carried the day.
Every gadget I've shown you's like *them* in
some way.

"Except *for just one little invention I've
been saving for last. It's a super-fantastic
ELECTRIC JUMPING BABY CARRIAGE
I invented all by myself. Give up, Ernie?"*

"*I never give up, Bert.*"